Giggles and Joy

Spiritual Life Lessons
for Kids

Ariane de Bonvoisin
Carlie Sutcliffe
Illustrated by Ellie Cross

For Everest, my little biggest love of my life,
For Alfie, my biggest big love of my life,

And for all the children of the world.

You are pure love, pure light, pure magic.
May you always remember your perfection.

All my love,
Ariane

ISBN: 978-0-9776808-1-8

Library of Congress: 2017916353

Published by:
Ariane Media LLC
New York, NY USA
www.arianedebonvoisin.com
www.gigglesandjoy.com

FIRST EDITION

Printed in Canada

Advance Praise for *Giggles and Joy*

"The biggest gift you can give your children is to remind them of their spiritual nature.
The Giggles and Joy book series does exactly that!"
—Lisa Miller, PhD, author of *The Spiritual Child*

"The Giggles and Joy series highlights for children what is good, true and beautiful, in our world,
and in themselves. Sweet reads that inspire and delight!"
—Susan Stiffelman, author of *Parenting with Presence* (an Eckhart Tolle Edition)

"The delightful Giggles and Joy series will inspire kids everywhere to live boldly, joyfully, and consciously."
—Stephen Powers, Grammy-winning producer, father of 3, CEO of Bodhi Tree

"*Giggles and Joy* connects children to the direct source of self-worth and self-reliance existing right within their own inner
spirit. I highly recommend it for anchoring children in a spiritually healthy sense of self and relating to their world."
—Michael Bernard Beckwith, author of *Life Visioning* and founder of Agape International Spiritual Center

"Regardless of the spiritual path you follow, there is a treasure trove for children in these pages."
—Barnet Bain, author of *The Book of Doing and Being*, director of *Milton's Secret*

"These books are fun while being packed with meaning and life wisdom."
—Isla Fisher, award-winning actress

"The Giggles and Joy series is a great addition to my favorite books that instill real self-worth and
universal values of kindness, compassion and love, in my kids!"
—Michelle Gale, mindfulness teacher and author of *Mindful Parenting in a Messy World*

"I hope many parents and teachers consider these books a must-read for their little ones."
—Karen Salmansohn, best-selling author of *Think Happy*

"The Giggles and Joy series introduces young kids to a set of universal spiritual ideas and values
that are so important to the development of character and kindness."
—Jonathan Fields, founder of Good Life Project®

Introduction

I've always believed that from any tough situation, something good will come. This book is the proof.

On September 12th, 2013, I became a mother to a beautiful blue-eyed boy. He remained without a name for nearly a month while my husband and I waited to get some clues and guidance from him as to his name.

We called him Everest.

Now Everest had different plans from the ones that we had for him. I imagined he'd be the perfect Buddha baby. I'd had a beautiful, easy pregnancy and wonderful birth. I'd done everything a girl could do from yoga to meditation, and used every other spiritual tool I'd come across. I considered myself firmly committed to raise a 'conscious child.' So, when Everest decided not to sleep for the first 18 MONTHS of his life, I thought I might just go crazy.

To him, his name was 'Never Rest,' not Everest!

In my attempt to get him back to sleep, even just for a few hours at a time, I tried everything—including the poems you now hold in your hands. The one thing that did seem to settle him, make him feel loved, safe and able to rest was my husband and me telling him these special words.

While my face and body revealed the impact of no sleep for that long, my heart and soul soared at the opportunity to instill some extraordinary beliefs, life skills, reminders and guidance for this beautiful soul.

Today, age 4, Everest sleeps beautifully but still asks me for a poem every night. Or two. 'One more Mommy.' 'Last one.' 'Last more!'

One day, on a plane from the US to Cape Town, I thought: 'Why not share these with other parents?' This book is a humble attempt to instill joy, love, confidence and a reminder of their amazing presence into the youngest of hearts. I believe when we treat children of all ages with honesty, respect and true awareness, they will flourish and thrive.

This book is for anyone—parents, grandparents, godparents, teachers, friends and care-givers of the world's children—those of us who have the magical task of guiding and reminding them of their light and their true divine nature. Feel free to read them at bedtime or at any time, to change a few words around, add to them and ask the child what this means to them. Pick a theme for the day or the week. This book is yours to explore.

Some poems are happy and funny. Some are more serious and deep. Some rhyme beautifully, while some are just simple to read. Some touch upon important themes children will face and some give them skills to navigate this world.

They are 'spiritual' in that they are imbued with love, optimism, humor, honesty and common sense. They are not for or against any religion. They do not promote or offend anyone's sense of God, a Divine Being, Life or the Universe.

They do leave an impact on anyone who reads or hears them by expanding our hearts and touching on why we are on this planet, what's important and also what's possible.

While I've read these poems to my son from birth, kids up to the age of 10 will appreciate them and be able to read them. The impact will remain with them throughout their childhood, and hopefully beyond.

Many of us are looking for ways to keep the purity and heart-centered joy of our kids alive, while still preparing them for this world. We want to keep their spirit, their potential and their innate wisdom intact. We want to share lessons that we've taken a lifetime to learn. Many of us walk a spiritual path in some form or another. Many of us would like to be that example and share it with our children.

This book hopes to give you a tool to do just that.

Love and Blessings,
Ariane

Giggles and Joy

Deep down inside you
Live two special friends.
Always together,
Their love never ends.
One is a little girl,
The other a boy—
Let me introduce you to
Giggles and Joy!

Sometimes you laugh
From a tickle or a stroke.
Or a fart sound sneaks out
When you hear a good joke.
Out jumps a feeling,
Keen to burst free—
That's Giggles and Joy
Making you happy, you see!

And yet there are times
When you feel rather sad.
Or something goes wrong
That makes you quite mad.
On days when you're like this,
When your nerves start to fray,
Giggles and Joy
Seem a long way away.

But like most friends we have,
They need to be asked
To come out and play,
Or to help with a task.
So don't ever forget
They're right there inside—
Bring them out in the open,
Let them come for the ride.

Remember this now
As you drift off to sleep:
That Giggles and Joy
Are best friends to keep.
They love being with you,
They're the easiest way
To feel happy and grateful
For this perfect day.

Kindness

Kindness is sharing your snack with someone who doesn't have one.
Kindness is holding the door open for someone to let them in.

Kindness is helping someone who is hurt.
Kindness is thinking about other people's feelings.

Kindness is sharing your umbrella when it's raining so no one has to get wet.
Kindness is saying, 'I'm sorry' when you know you've hurt someone's feelings.

Kindness is being gentle and loving to animals.
Kindness is finding the perfect present for someone you love.

Kindness is helping Mom or Dad clean up the kitchen after supper.
Kindness is sharing your toys, even when you don't want to.

Kindness is forgiving, letting things go and giving someone another chance.
Kindness is giving someone a hug and a kiss if you see they're feeling a bit sad.

Kindness is noticing someone needs a bit of money and giving them a coin.
Kindness is listening and taking turns to speak.

Kindness is inviting the new kid at school to play with you.
Kindness is taking care of planet Earth and picking up any rubbish.

Home

Home isn't the four walls of your bedroom or your address.
It isn't where Mom or Dad or your grandparents live either.
Home is much bigger than all that you see,
It's where your character, your love and your heart all can be.

Home is where you find yourself right now,
A place deep inside of you that makes you feel safe.
Everywhere is your home if you can see all that space,
Planet Earth is so special—there's no need to stay in one place!

Home is where you are happy and sad, where you can laugh and cry,
Where you are eating and sleeping, playing and singing.
Home is where you are by yourself, or with family and friends.
Home is where love never ends.

Home is where you are being you,
Where you don't have to change yourself to fit in.
Home is where you feel special and warm,
A place where there's no need to perform.

Home is where all of you can exist,
Where you know you are perfect and protected.
Your outside home can be different and change,
But your internal home will always be the same.

Sleep Is The Best

Sleep, sleep, sleep is the best,
The time of the day when you finally rest.
Shut your eyes nice and gently,
Let you breath start to slow,
Because this is the time your body will grow.

Sleep, sleep, sleep is the best,
Food left in your tummy will always digest.
It feeds your whole body,
You'll get big and strong,
Your hair and your nails will grow,
Healthy and long.

Sleep, sleep, sleep is the best,
Your heart keeps on beating deep down in your chest.
Blood pumps through your body,
As you lie oh so still,
Perfectly working so you rarely fall ill.

Sleep, sleep, sleep is the best,
Snuggled warm and cosy,
Tucked up in your nest.
In your dreams God will find you,
And make everything right,
So you wake in the morning
Feeling happy and light.

Sleep, sleep, sleep is the best,
But take a moment or two
To think as you rest.
You have people who love you
In good times and bad,
Friends and family around you
When you're happy or sad.

Sleep, sleep, sleep is the best,
A time to remember that
You're truly blessed.
Be grateful for everything
That happened this day.
For the laughs and the lessons,
Give thanks as you pray.

Your Body Is Your Best Friend

Your body is your best friend,
It loves you without doubt.
It only asks one thing from you
That you love it inside and out.

Your body is a crazy thing
Made up of special parts.
Hair, bones, skin and muscles
Are really just the start.

For tucked inside your body
Are organs you can't see.
The parts that keep on working
Even when you're fast asleep.

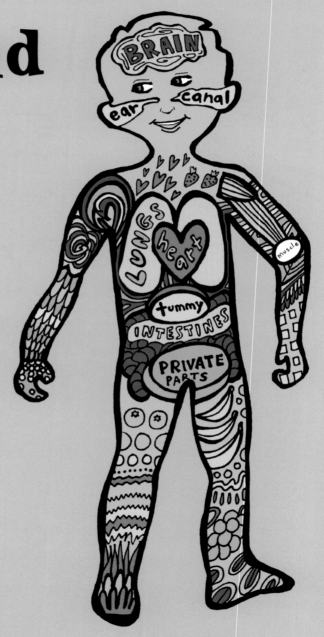

Give it lots of sleep at night,
Let go of any stress.
Lie still in bed with happy thoughts
So all of you can rest.

And when you're up and wide awake
Make sure you treat it well.
Eat healthy fruits and vegetables
To nourish every cell.

Keep your body private,
It's not for you to share.
Unless you're with someone you trust,
Don't show your bottom bare!

Your body knows the answers,
The truth lies deep inside.
Keep quiet and just listen,
Your heart will be your guide.

Remember that your body
Was made with care and love.
Respect it and protect it,
Give thanks to God above.

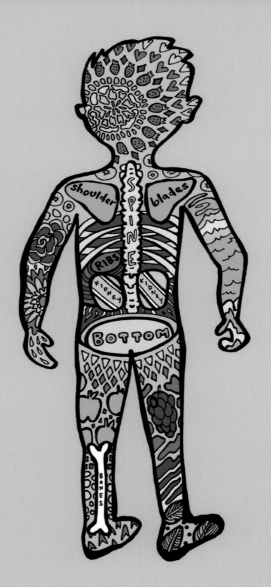

Bye Bye Bad Day

When you woke up this morning
The day stretched ahead.
You thought of the fun things
So you bounced out of bed.
But often the good times
Are mixed with some bad.
So you woke up happy
But went to bed sad.

You might think you're alone
In feeling this way.
You look at your friends
While they happily play.
But we all have those days
When things don't work out.
We all have those days
When we cry or we shout.

But there's something important
That happens each day.
It makes little difference
If it's sunny or gray.
Because in all that we do
Hides a lesson, you see.
It's there to be found
And that is the key.

So when things go wrong
Or not as you thought,
Look back through your day,
Find the lesson it taught.
If a friend said mean things
Or ignored you all day,
Remember this next time
You behave the same way.

There's always some good
To be found in each day.
Even when sometimes
It seems far from that way.
Just think of the people
You love without doubt,
Think of the people
You can't live without.

There's a very big chance
They also love you.
They're stuffed full of love
From their hat to their shoe.
Be grateful and happy
They spent part of their day,
Right there by your side
Sometimes guiding the way.

The last thing to say
As you drift off to sleep,
Remember these bad days
Are for no one to keep.
Blow them away
Like bubbles in the air.
Wrap them up in tight bundles
Keep them locked away there.

Don't let a bad day
Make you sad and upset.
Put it out of your head
Let your heart forget.
Remember the good things
Let those memories stay.
Lie your head on your pillow,
Whisper, 'Bye bye bad day.'

Prayer

Prayer is the answer to it all.
When you talk to God, you are never alone.
God listens to your every word,
So know that God can handle anything, big or small.

Pray with your whole heart, for yourself or someone else.
You can pray for anything that is important to you.
Watch the miracles that happen each day,
So all you have to do is remember God is on your team.

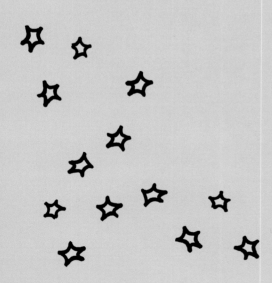

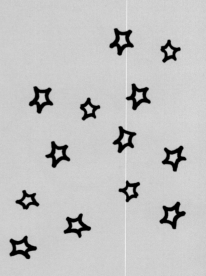

God loves everyone, as God loves you.
There's no one on Earth who's not loved.
Some days are good and then some are bad,
So pray when you're happy and pray when you're down.

Everything happens according to God's perfect plan,
So rest and say Yes to what is happening now.
Prayer is a way to say thank you and ask for what you need,
So that God can guide you and show you the way.

Prayer doesn't mean you get exactly what you want.
God always knows what is best and what is right.

We all need to learn and grow and love,
So try to make praying an
Important part of your day.

Mother Earth

This world is filled with adventures for you to start
To explore, learn, have fun and share your heart.

You can climb mountains
Or walk through the woods.
You can run on the beach
Or sit and think of all that is good.

You can jump in the ocean
Or dive deep beneath the waves.
You can sit and do nothing,
Just stare out and gaze.

You can go and be alone
Or play with your best friend.
You can lie on your back,
Look up at the day's end.
You can wake up early,
Watch the sun say, 'Hi.'
You can watch the flowers open
And reach up for the sky.

You can wrap up the day
And say thanks to it all.
Go to sleep peacefully,
Curled up in a ball.
Know that tomorrow
Everything will be there,
That Mother Earth and Mama Ocean
Will bring another day beyond compare.

Mother Earth and Mama Ocean are
Best friends every day.
They work hard to make this world
A beautiful place to play.

Remember to greet them the next
Time you go out and race.
They give you food, air,
Beauty and grace.
Be gentle with them and say,
'Thank you' for all they do,
For this blue planet we live on is
Something very special for you.

Ariane de Bonvoisin is a writer, speaker and entrepreneur. Her commitment is to serve her fellow human beings and live consciously in this beautiful world. She has a passion for travel and true self-discovery and considers herself a global soul. Her two loves are her partner Alfie and her son Everest. Their presence has woken up a deep desire to share more love, magic and inner peace through all aspects of her work. These books are a testament to that intention.

Carlie Sutcliffe, a writer living in Cape Town, is married and has a grown-up son. Her love for poetry came when she discovered the rhythm and silliness of rhyme to be the perfect way to disguise a serious message. Carlie met Ariane in Cape Town when Ariane was pregnant. Their love of writing was the catalyst to a beautiful friendship. These poems are a dedication to their wonderful sons.

Ellie Cross is interested in using art as a problem–solving tool to create a more just and loving world. Originally from Seattle, she has led community art projects and painted murals in Asia and Africa, as well as North and Central America. Ellie is inspired by the fearless creativity of children and illustrates in a whimsical style designed to engage their abundant imaginations.